Music Express Songbook

Years 1-2

Series devised by **Maureen Hanke**

Songs arranged by **Michael Haslam**

Illustrations by **Alison Dexter**

First published 2003
by A&C Black Publishers Ltd
37 Soho Square, London W1D 3QZ
© 2003 A&C Black Publishers Ltd
ISBN 0 7136 6782-6

Series devised by Maureen Hanke
Unit headings © Qualifications and Curriculum Authority, 2000
Series designed by Jocelyn Lucas
Cover illustration © Alex Ayliffe 2002
Inside illustrations © Alison Dexter 2003
Music setting by Jeanne Fisher
Edited by Marie Penny

A&C Black uses paper produced with elemental chlorine-free
pulp, harvested from managed sustainable forests.

Printed in Great Britain by Martins The Printers Ltd,
Berwick upon Tweed

Contents

Songs: Year One

Sounds interesting
Sound song (track 1a)	4
Hands can hold (track 2)	5
Choose an instrument (track 4)	6
Listen to the East (track 5)	7
The wheels on the bus (track 8)	8
Sing a song of people (track 10)	9

The long and the short of it
Some sounds are short (track 12)	10
It's bonfire night (track 15)	11
Fade or float (track 16)	12
Ho! Jack Frost (track 18)	13
Coming down (track 19)	14

Feel the pulse
Pinocchio (track 21)	16
Okki-tokki-unga (track 25)	17
I hear thunder (track 28)	18
This old man (track 32)	19
Clap your hands (track 37)	20

Taking off
Five little froggies (track 42)	21
Slide song (track 43)	22
Jack's song (track 44)	22
Miss Mary Mac (track 45)	23
Hot cross buns (track 49)	24
Pease pudding hot (track 50)	24

What's the score (tracks from CD 2)
I am the music man (track 1)	25
Bang, bang the sticks go bang (track 2)	26
I can see coconuts (track 5)	27
Slowly, slowly, very slowly (track 6)	28
When you play the tambour (track 8)	29
Jenny tap the sticks (track 9)	29
Silence and sound (track 11)	30
Yo ho ho! (track 13)	30

Rain, rain go away
Says the bee (track 18)	31
Lots of worms (track 19)	31
Rillaby rill (track 21)	32
Shall I sing?/Rain, rain go away (track 26)	33

Songs: Year Two

The long and the short of it

Some sounds are short (track 1)	10
Dipidu (track 2)	36
Jackass wid him long tail (track 3)	37
Tinga layo (track 10)	38
Mi caballo (track 15)	40

Feel the pulse

Down the avenue (track 19)	42
Kye kye kule (track 21)	43
Someone's in the kitchen (track 22)	44
How many people? (track 30)	46

Taking off

I jump out of bed (track 35)	47
Looby Loo (track 36)	48
Six little ducks (track 37)	49
The Prehistoric animal brigade (track 39)	50
Fossils (track 44)	52

What's the score

Make your sound like mine (track 46)	53
Sound puzzle (track 47)	53
Start conducting (track 49)	12
The Hairy Scary Castle (track 52)	54

Rain, rain go away

It's gonna be hot (track 54)	56
Majā Pade (track 57)	57
Gonna build a house boat (track 62)	58
Noah's ark (track 64)	59

Sounds interesting

Post calypso (track 68)	60
Just a load of rubbish (track 69)	61
Sally go round the sun (track 70)	61
Teatime shout (track 71)	62
When I go to bed (track 73)	63

Using Music Express as a scheme of work

Music Express fulfils the requirements of the Music National Curriculum of England, of Wales and of Northern Ireland and the 5-14 National Guidelines for Scotland.

Learning with *Music Express*, children will gain a broad and balanced musical education.

A steady progression plan has been built into *Music Express*, both within each book and from one year to the next, ensuring consistent musical development.

Music Express songbooks

This songbook has been specially created for music readers. It is designed to be used alongside the Music Express scheme or on its own. Containing all the songs from Music Express Years 1 and 2, it is a useful reference and performance resource for music specialist teachers.

Using this book

This book contains all the songs that appear in the Music Express Year 1 and Year 2 books, arranged for voice(s) and piano/guitar.

The songs are presented in the same order as they appear in Music Express Years 1 and 2 with the exception of 'Some sounds are short' (page 10) and 'Start conducting' (page 12). The track number next to the song title matches the CD track number in the scheme. (Where there are multiple tracks for a single song, the CD track number matches the complete or performance version.)

SOUND SONG

Version 1

Sounds we hear,	Sounds we hear,
Through the window,	Through the window,
Far and near,	Far and near,
Soft and still,	Soft and still,
High and low,	High and low,
Loud and clear,	Loud and clear,
Listen ...	
Listen ...	
Listen ...	
Listen ...	

Version 2

Sounds we hear,	Sounds we hear,
When we make them,	When we make them,
Far and near,	Far and near,
Soft and still,	Soft and still,
High and low,	High and low,
Loud and clear,	Loud and clear,
Listen to Bobbie ...	
Listen to Sanjay ...	
Listen to Alice ...	
Listen to Sam ...	

Words and music: Harriet Powell

HANDS CAN HOLD

Vs 1 Hands can hold and hands can *squeeze*,
Hands can rest upon your *knees*,
Hands can clap and hands can shake,
What *kind* of sound can your hands
make?

Vs 2 Hands can hold and hands can *squeeze*,
Hands can rest upon our *knees*,
Hands can clap and hands can shake,
This is the *sound* which our hands make.

Words: Veronica Clark
Music: Traditional

CHOOSE AN INSTRUMENT

Version 1

Vs 1 Choose an instrument you can play,
You can play, you can play,
Choose an instrument you can play,
What's your favourite?

Vs 2 You can play the tambourine,
Tambourine, tambourine,
You can play the tambourine,
That's your favourite.

Version 2

Vs 1 Choose an instrument you can play,
You can play, you can play,
Choose an instrument you can play,
What's your favourite?

Vs 2 You can play and play and STOP,
Play and STOP, play and STOP,
You can play and play and STOP,
Play and STOP it.

Words: Sue Nicholls
Music: Traditional

(2nd verse, version 2)

LISTEN TO THE EAST

Vs 1 Listen to the east,
Listen to the west,
Listen to the sound and play
The listening test.

Vs 2 Play it to the east,
Play it to the west,
Play us all the instrument
That sounds the best.

Words and music: Sheena Roberts

THE WHEELS ON THE BUS

Vs 1 The wheels on the bus go round
and round,
Round and round, round and round,
The wheels on the bus go round
and round,
All day long.

Vs 2 The bell on the bus goes ding, ding,
ding ...

Vs 3 The babies on the bus all clap their
hands ...

Music: Traditional
Arrangement: Playsongs Publications

SING A SONG OF PEOPLE

Sing a song, sing a song of people,
Sing a song, walking fast or slow;
Sing a song, sing a song of people,
People in the city, up and down they go.

Sing a song, sing a song of people,
Sing a song, walking fast or slow;
Sing a song, sing a song of people,
People in the city, up and down they go.

Words: Lois Lenski
Music: Chris Cameron

Sing_ a song, sing a song of peo - ple,

Sing_ a song, walk-ing fast or slow; Sing_ a song, sing a song of peo - ple,

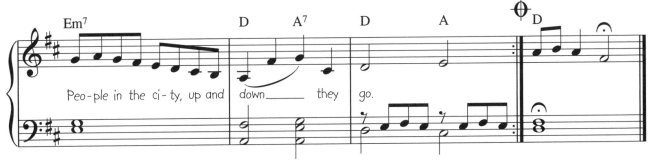

Peo-ple in the ci - ty, up and down____ they go.

SOME SOUNDS ARE SHORT

Some sounds are short,
Some sounds are long,
Which sound will you make
After this song?

Some sounds are short,
Some sounds are long,
You made a (short/long) sound,
After the song.

Words: Sue Nicholls
Music: Traditional

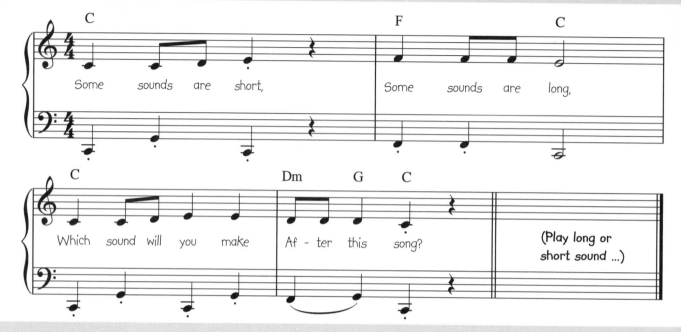

SOME SOUNDS ARE SHORT

Some sounds are short,
Some sounds are long,
Which sounds are on the card
After this song?

Some sounds are short,
Some sounds are long,
These sounds were on the card
After the song.

Words: Sue Nicholls
Music: Traditional

IT'S BONFIRE NIGHT

Ch It's bonfire night,
It's bonfire night,
It's bonfire night,
And the sky is bright.

Vs 1 See the catherine wheel,
Listen to the sound.
See the catherine wheel,
Listen to the sound.

Ch It's bonfire night ...

Vs 2 See the banger,
Listen to the sound ...

Ch It's bonfire night ...

Vs 3 See the rocket,
Listen to the sound ...

Ch It's bonfire night ...

Words and music: Leslie Lees

FADE OR FLOAT?

Take a beater, strike a note,
Strike a note, strike a note,
In the air the sound might float,
Or fade quickly.

(Pause to allow a child to choose an instrument and
predict the length of the sound.)

Take a beater, strike a note ...

Words: Sue Nicholls
Music: Traditional

START CONDUCTING

Vs 1 Pass the cards around the ring,
Round the ring, round the ring,
Pass the cards around the ring,
You're conducting.

Vs 2 Choose a picture, put it down,
Put it down, put it down,
Choose another, put it down.
Start conducting.

Words: Helen MacGregor
Music: Traditional

For more songs like this visit www.acblack.com/musicexpress

HO! JACK FROST

Who turns the trees all silver white?
Ho! Jack Frost.
Who helps us make a slippery slide?
Ho! Jack Frost.
Who comes so silent through the night
  and scatters crystals sharp and bright?
Who paints the windows snowy white?
Ho! Jack Frost.

Words: Helen Call
Music: Mary Root Kern

Vs 1 Watching fireworks, catherine wheels
    spin round,
  Sparks fall to the ground,
  They go spinning and flying around,
  They go spinning and flying around.

(Instrumental break)

Vs 2 Falling raindrops, make a tiny sound,
  As they hit the ground,
  They come pittering, pattering down,
  They come pittering, pattering down.

(Instrumental break)

Vs 3 Catching snowflakes before they touch
    the ground,
  Before they touch the ground,
  They go swirling and whirling around,
  They go swirling and whirling around.

(Instrumental break)

Vs 4 Frozen puddles, on the icy ground,
  Hear the crackling sound,
  As we step on the ice all around,
  As we step on the ice all around.

(Instrumental break)

Words and music: Jill Darby

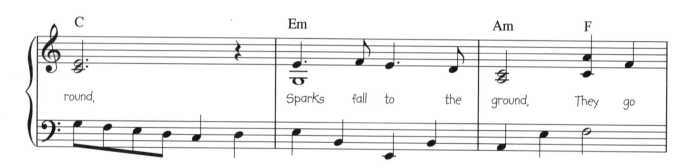

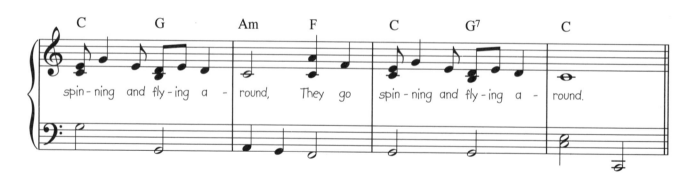

Vs 1 My name is Pinocchio.
I am in a puppet show,
I can move my wooden arm,
 it goes like this.
Here is what my arm can do,
 see if you can do it too,
Here is what my arm can do,
 it goes like this.

Vs 2 My name is Pinocchio.
I am in a puppet show,
I can nod my wooden head ...

Vs 3 My name is Pinocchio.
I am in a puppet show,
I can tap my wooden feet ...

Variation (Pinocchio's band)

My name is Pinocchio.
I am in a music show,
I can play a magic drum,
 it goes like this.
Here is what my drum can do,
 see if you can do it too,
(All drummers)
Dum dum dum dum dum dum dum,
 it goes like this. ...

Words: Kaye Umansky
Music: Traditional

OKKI-TOKKI-UNGA

Ch Okki-tokki-unga,
Okki-tokki-unga,
Hey, Missa day, Missa doh,
Missa day. (repeat)

Vs 1 Hexa cola misha woni,
Hexa cola misha woni,
Hexa cola misha woni. (repeat)

Introduction and chorus

I HEAR THUNDER

I hear thunder
I hear thunder
Hark don't you?
Hark don't you?
Pitter patter raindrops
Pitter patter raindrops
I'm wet through!
So are you!

THIS OLD MAN

Version 1

This old man,
He played one,
He played nick nack
On my drum with a
Nick nack paddy wack
Give the dog a bone,
This old man came
Rolling home.

Version 2

This old man,
He played one,
He played nick nack
On my drum with a
*[1   2   3   4]
Give the dog a bone,
This old man came
Rolling home.

* Improvise in the four silent beats

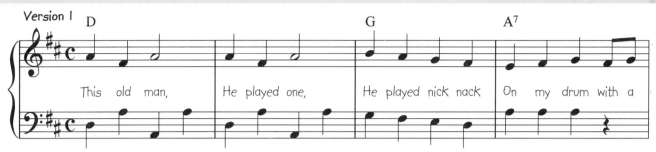

Version 1

This old man,   He played one,   He played nick nack   On my drum with a

Nick nack pad-dy wack   Give the dog a bone,   This old man came   Roll - ing home.

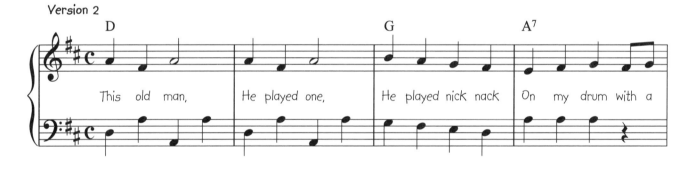

Version 2

This old man,   He played one,   He played nick nack   On my drum with a

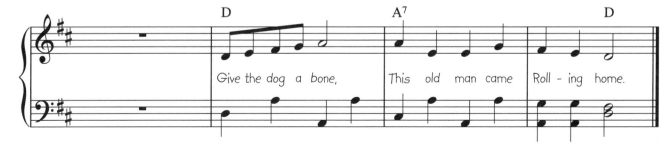

Give the dog a bone,   This old man came   Roll - ing home.

CLAP YOUR HANDS

Clap your hands and wiggle your fingers,
Clap your hands and wiggle your fingers,
Clap your hands and wiggle your fingers,
Now we've made a pattern.

Words: Sue Nicholls
Music: Traditional

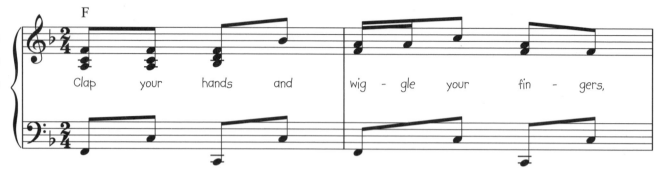

Clap your hands and wig - gle your fin - gers,

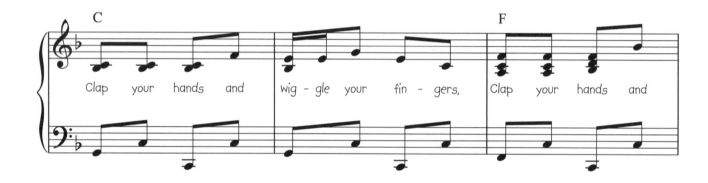

Clap your hands and wig - gle your fin - gers, Clap your hands and

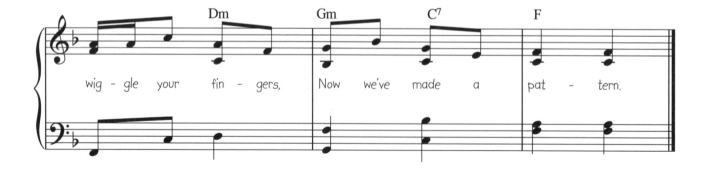

wig - gle your fin - gers, Now we've made a pat - tern.

FIVE LITTLE FROGGIES

Five little froggies sitting on a well,
One leaned over and down she fell,
Froggies jump high,
Froggies jump low,
Four little froggies
Jumping to and fro.

Four little froggies sitting on a well ...

Three little froggies ...

Two little froggies ... etc

Music: Helen MacGregor

21

SLIDE SONG

In the park,
There are stairs
Climb each one,
Take great care
At the top,
It's your ride
Hold on tight!
Slide.

Words and music: Sue Nicholls

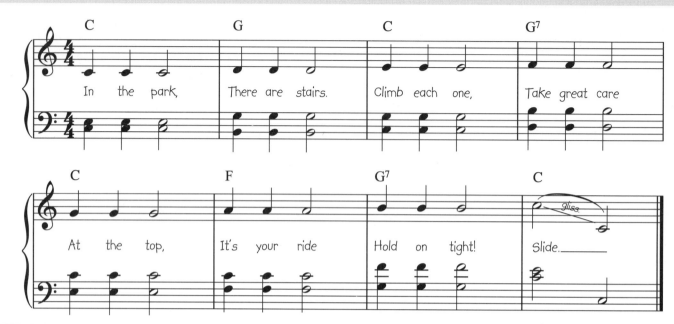

JACK'S SONG

(1) Is Jack climbing up the beanstalk?
(2) Is Jack climbing down the beanstalk?
(3) Is he hiding, keeping still?
    (Listen!)

(Play line (1), (2) or (3) again)

Words and music: Helen MacGregor

Miss Mary Mac, Mac, Mac,
All dressed in *black, black, black,*
With silver buttons, buttons, buttons,
All down her *back, back, back.*

Miss   Ma – ry   Mac   Mac   Mac

Mac,   Mac,   Mac. All   dressed   in   black,   black,

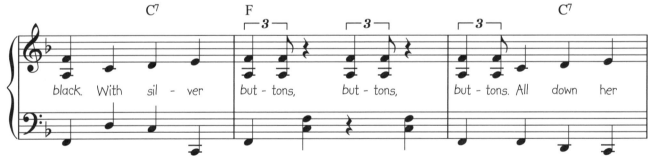

black. With   sil – ver   but – tons,   but – tons,   but – tons. All   down   her

back,   back,   back.

HOT CROSS BUNS

Hot cross buns
Hot cross buns
One a penny, two a penny,
Hot cross buns.
If you have no daughters,
Give them to your sons,
One a penny, two a penny,
Hot cross buns.

Words and music: Traditional

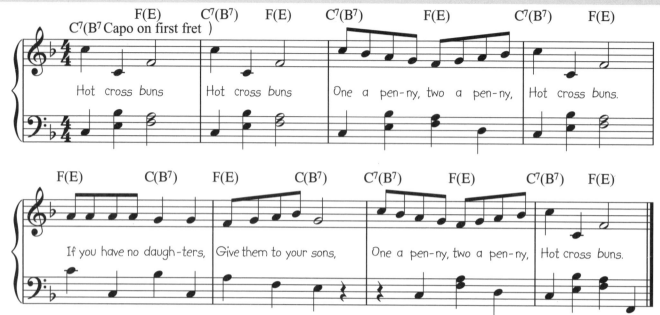

PEASE PUDDING HOT

Pease pudding hot,
Pease pudding cold,
Pease pudding in the pot,
Nine days old.

Words and music: Traditional

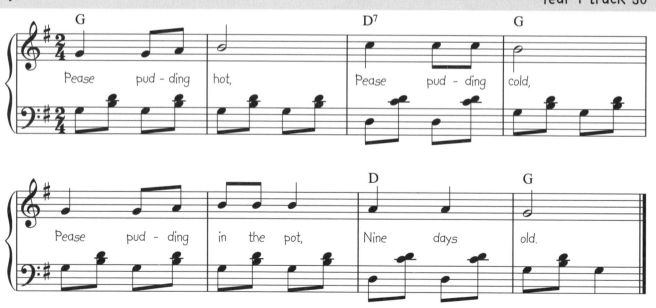

I AM THE MUSIC MAN

I am the music man,
I come from far away,
And I can play.
What can you play?

(Child picks an instrument.)

I play the tambourine.

(Child plays while all sing.)

Shake-a shake-a shake-a shake,
Shake-a shake, shake-a shake,
Shake-a shake-a shake-a shake,
Shake-a shake-a shake.

BANG, BANG, THE STICKS GO BANG

Vs 1 Bang, bang, the sticks go bang!
Play as loudly as you can,
Now as quietly as a mouse,
Creeping softly round the house.

Vs 2 Shake, shake the shakers shake
Play the loudest sound they make
Now as quietly ...

Vs 3 Boom, boom the drums go boom
Play them loudly in this room ...

Vs 4 Ting, ting the bells go ting
Play them loudly make them ring ...

Words: Sue Nicholls

I CAN SEE COCONUTS

I can see coconuts up in the tree.
Coconut water inside them for me.
Let's collect coconuts,
 one, two, three, four,
Shake the tree, shake the tree,
I'd like some more.

One, two, three, four, five, six,
 seven, eight, nine, ten.
One, two, three, four, five, six,
 seven, eight, nine, ten.

Words: Wendy van Blakenstsein; adapted by
  Helen MacGregor
Music: Wendy van Blankenstein

SLOWLY, SLOWLY

Vs 1 Slowly, slowly, very slowly
Creeps the garden snail.
Slowly, slowly, very slowly
Up the wooden rail.

Vs 2 Quickly, quickly, very quickly
Runs the little mouse.
Quickly, quickly, very quickly
Round about the house.

Words: Traditional
Music: A W I Chitty

WHEN YOU PLAY THE TAMBOUR

When you play the tambour,
What sound will you make?
Using hand or beater,
Tap or slide or scrape.

Words: Sue Nicholls
Music: Traditional

JENNY, TAP THE STICKS

(Jenny), tap the sticks,
Tap them very loudly,
(Jenny), tap the sticks,
Tap them very loudly.

(Jenny), tap the sticks,
Tap them very quietly,
(Jenny), tap the sticks,
Tap them very quietly.

Words: Sue Nicholls
Music: Traditional

29

SILENCE AND SOUND

Use the cards, change them round,
Some show silence, some show sound,
So our music changes in a clever way.
Who will show us what to play?

Words: Sue Nicholls
Music: Traditional

YO HO HO

Yo ho ho, me mates,
A pirate's life for me,
Off to find a treasure chest,
On an island in the sea.

Words: Helen MacGregor
Music: Traditional

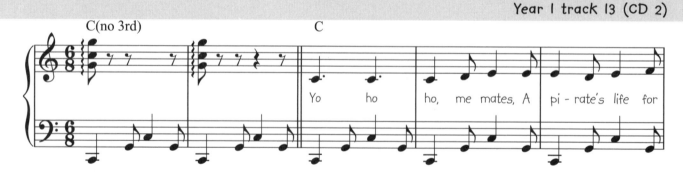

SAYS THE BEE

Vs 1 Come with me, says the bee,
Into the daffodil.
All our house has yellow walls,
And honey on the sill.

Vs 2 Come with me, says the bee,
Into the open rose.
Perfume curtains all around,
And pollen on your toes.

Vs 3 Come with me, says the bee,
Into the lily flower.
Sun in your window every sunny day,
Umbrella for a shower.

Words and music: Malvina Reynolds

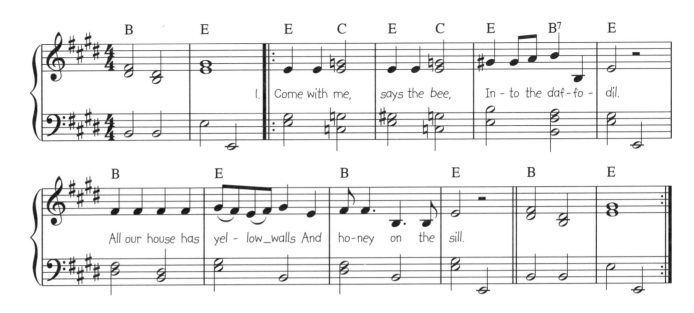

Well, there are lots of worms
  way under the ground,
Lots of worms that I've never found,
I'll bet they're way down there
  a-diggin' around
Way under the ground.

Words and music: Patty Zeitlin

RILLABY RILL

Grasshoppers three a-fiddling went,
Hey ho never *be still*,
They paid no money toward the rent,
But all day long with their *elbows bent*,
They fiddled a tune called rillaby rillaby
Fiddled a tune called rillaby rill.

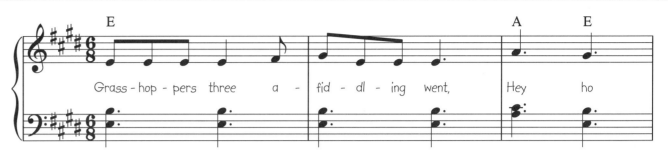

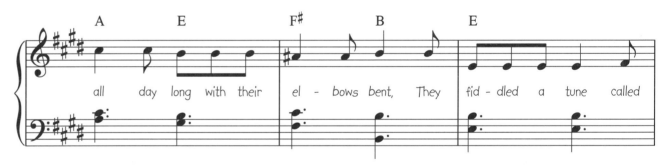

Shall I sing? says the lark,
Shall I bloom? says the flower,
Shall I come? says the sun,
Shall I fall? says the shower.

Rain rain go away,
Come again another day.

Shall I buzz? says the bee,
Shall I bloom? says the flower,
Shall I wiggle? says the worm,
Shall I fall? says the shower.

Rain rain go away,
Come again another day.

Shall I hop? says the grasshopper,
Shall I bloom? says the flower,
Shall I march? says the ant,
Shall I fall? says the shower.

Rain rain go away
Come again another day

Words: adapted from traditional by Helen MacGregor
& Sheena Roberts
Music: Neville Favell

B

Rain, rain go a - way.

Come a - gain an - oth - er day.

(Sh)

DIPIDU

Good day, good day to you,
Good day, oh dipidu.
Good day, good day to you,
Good day, oh dipidu.

Dip, dip, dipidu,
Dipidu, oh dipidu,
Dip, dip, dip, dip, dipidu,
Dipidu, oh dipidu.

Words and music: Traditional African

SOME SOUNDS ARE SHORT (track 1) is on page 10

Jackass wid him long tail,
Bag a coco comin down.
Jackass wid him long tail,
Bag a coco coming down.
 No tease him, no worry him,
 No mek de hamper squeeze him.
Jackass wid him long tail,
Bag a coco comin down.

Words and melody: Traditional Jamaican

TINGA LAYO

Ch Tinga layo, come, little donkey, come.
Tinga layo, come, little donkey, come.

Vs 1 Me donkey eat, me donkey sleep,
Me donkey kick wid him two hind feet.
Me donkey eat, me donkey sleep,
Me donkey kick wid him two hind feet.

Ch Tinga layo, come, little donkey, come ...

Vs 2 Me donkey walk, me donkey talk,
Me donkey eat wid a spoon and fork.
Me donkey walk, me donkey talk,
Me donkey kick wid a spoon and fork.

Ch Tinga layo, come, little donkey, come ...

Words and music: Traditional Caribbean

Introduction

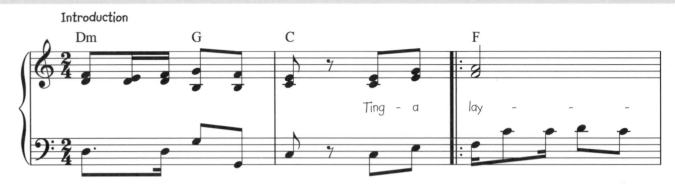

1. Me don - key eat, me don - key sleep, Me don - key

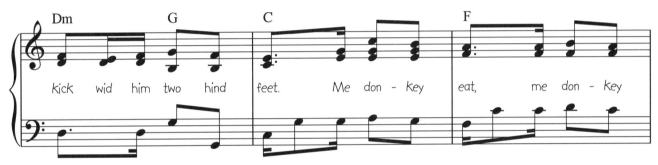

kick wid him two hind feet. Me don - key eat, me don - key

sleep, Me don - key kick wid him two hind feet. Ting - a

MI CABALLO BLANCO

Vs   As brilliant as the sunrise,
My horse is white as snow,
A friend that's ever faithful,
Riding together we will go.

Ch   Mi caballo, mi caballo,
Galopando va,
Mi caballo, mi caballo,
Galopando va.
Se - vay - se -va.
Se - vay - se -va, mm.

Attrib: Francisco Flores del Campo

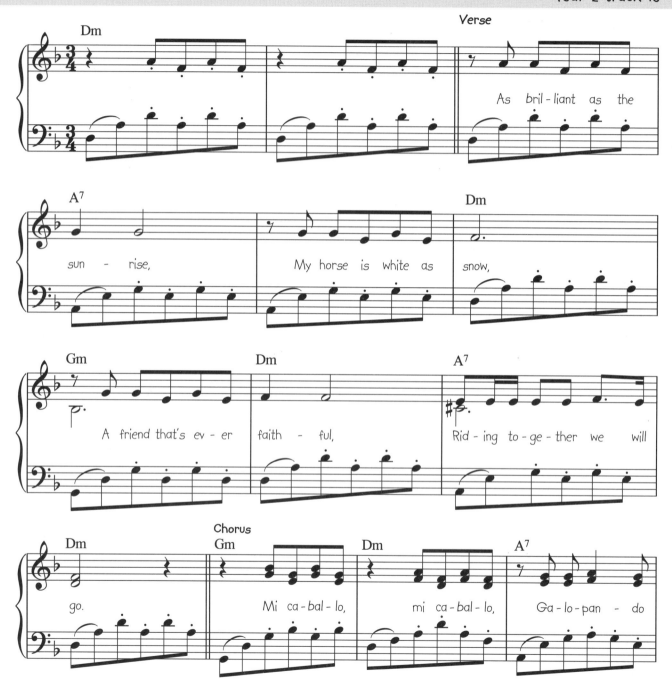

DOWN THE AVENUE

Vs 1 Grandpa's strolling down the avenue,
Grandpa's strolling down the avenue,
Grandpa's strolling down the avenue,
Strolling down the avenue with me.

Vs 2 Grown-ups striding down the avenue ...
Striding down the avenue with me.

Vs 3 My friend's running down the avenue ...
Running down the avenue with me.

Words: Sue Nicholls
Music: Traditional

1st verse very slow, 2nd verse faster, 3rd verse very fast

1. Grand - pa's stroll - ing down the av - en - ue,

Grand - pa's stroll - ing down the av - en - ue,

Grand - pa's stroll - ing down the av - en - ue,

Stroll - ing down the av - en - ue with me.

KYE KYE KULE

Call:

Kye Kye Kule,

Kye Kye Kofi nsa,

Kofi nsa langa,

Kaka shi langa,

Kum adende

Response:

Kye Kye Kule,

Kye Kye Kofi nsa,

Kofi nsa langa,

Kaka shi langa,

Kum adende

All (together) : Kum adende. Hey!

Words and melody: Traditional Akan

SOMEONE'S IN THE KITCHEN WITH DINAH

Vs Someone's in the kitchen with Dinah,
Someone's in the kitchen I know I know,
Someone's in the kitchen with Dinah,
Strumming on the old banjo.

Ch Fee, fie, fiddle-ee-i-o,
Fee, fie, fiddle-ee-i-o,
Fee, fie, fiddle-ee-i-o,
Strumming on the old banjo.

For more songs like this visit www.acblack.com/musicexpress

45

Vs 1 How many people here for dinner?
(Hands up!)
How many heard the dinner bell?
How many people here for dinner?
(Hands up!)
Roll up! Roll up! Roll up! sniff sniff
Mmmmmmmm! What's that smell?
Yorkshire pudding, Yorkshire pudding,
Yorkshire pudding, Yorkshire pudding.

Vs 2 How many people here for dinner? ...
Cauliflower cheese, cauliflower cheese ...

Vs 3 How many people here for dinner? ...
Baked banana, baked banana ...

Vs 4 How many people here for dinner?
(Hands up!)
How many heard the dinner bell?
How many people here for dinner?
(Hands up!)
Grub's up! Grub's up! Grub's up!
sniff sniff
Mmmmmmmm! Eat up well!

Words and music: Sheena Roberts

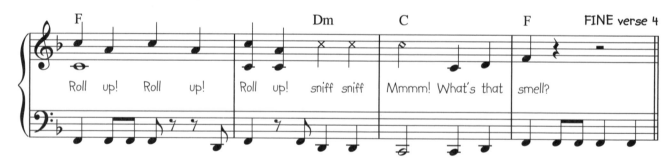

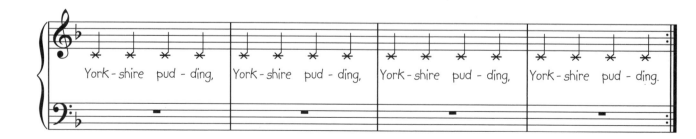

I JUMP OUT OF BED IN THE MORNING

Vs 1 I jump out of bed in the morning,
I jump out of bed in the morning,
I jump out of bed in the morning,
I hope it's a very nice day.

Vs 2 I jump out of bed and stretch
myself in the morning ...

Vs 3 I jump out of bed and stretch
myself, and step in the bath in
the morning ...

LOOBY LOO

Ch Here we go Looby Loo,
Here we go Looby Light,
Here we go Looby Loo,
All on a Saturday night.

Vs 1 First the tune jumps up,
Then it turns around,
Then it goes jogging and jumping,
Then it steps all the way down.

Ch Here we go Looby Loo,
Here we go Looby Light,
Here we go Looby Loo,
All on a Saturday night.

Vs 2 First your hand jumps up,
Then it turns around,
Then it goes jogging and jumping,
Then it steps all the way down.

Words: Traditional; verse 2: Helen MacGregor
Music: Traditional

SIX LITTLE DUCKS THAT I ONCE KNEW

Six little ducks that I once knew,
Fat ones, skinny ones, they were too.
But the one little duck with the
  feathers on his back,
He ruled the others with his
'Quack, quack, quack,
Quack, quack, quack.'
He ruled the others with his
'Quack, quack, quack!'

THE PREHISTORIC ANIMAL BRIGADE

Vs 1 Listen to the chorus
Of the brontosaurus,
And the stegosaurus,
Down by the swamp.

Vs 2 Along comes the dinosaur
Making such a loud roar,
Thumping with his feet
And going stomp, stomp, stomp.

Vs 3 Pterodactyl flapping,
Long beak clacking,
Big teeth snapping,
Down from the tree.

Vs 4 Here's a woolly mammoth,
Tusks all curly,
Joins the hurly burly,
Oh dear me!

What a noise!
It's the boys
Of the prehistoric animal brigade

What a noise!
It's the boys
Of the prehistoric animal brigade

Words and music: M L Reeve

Not too fast, like a dinosaur

FOSSILS

Fossils in the rock
Pterodactyl teeth
Millions of years
Made an ammonite.
Fossils in the rock
Pterodactyl teeth
Millions of years
Made an ammonite.

Words: Helen MacGregor
Melody: Saint-Saëns (adapted)

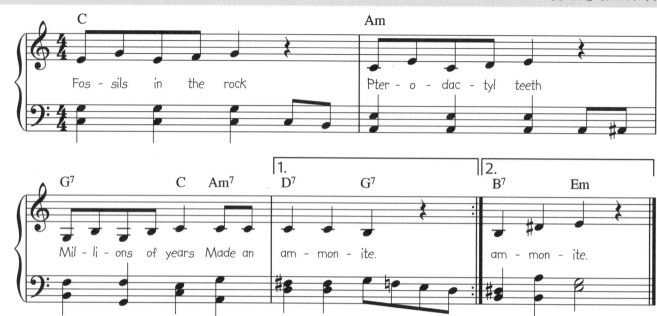

MAKE YOUR SOUND LIKE MINE

Make your sound
  the same as mine,
The same as mine,
  the same as mine.
Make your sound
  the same as mine,
And make it after me!

Words: Sue Nicholls
Music: Traditional

SOUND PUZZLE

Vs 1 Our sound puzzle is ready to be played,
Our sound puzzle is ready to be played,
Just stop and listen to every sound
that's made,
For our sound puzzle is ready to
be played.

Vs 2 Wood or metal, or is it made of skin?
Wood or metal, or is it made of skin?
Just stop and listen, your ears know
how to win,
Wood or metal, or is it made of skin?

Words: Sue Nicholls
Music: Traditional

START CONDUCTING (track 49) is on page 12

THE HAIRY SCARY CASTLE

In The Hairy Scary Castle,
In The Hairy Scary Castle,
In The Hairy Scary Castle,
    Where the *skeletons* RATTLE,
    And the ghosts go BOO!

In The Hairy Scary Castle ...
    Where the rats go SQUEAK,
    And the bats go FLAP!
    And the *skeletons* RATTLE,
    And the ghosts go BOO!

In The Hairy Scary Castle ...
    Where the stairs go CREAK
    And the clock goes TOCK!
    Where the rats go SQUEAK,
    And the bats go FLAP!
    And the *skeletons* RATTLE,
    And the ghosts go BOO!

In The Hairy Scary Castle ...
    Where the wind goes WHOOSH,
    And the doors go BANG!
    Where the stairs go CREAK
    And the clock goes TOCK!
    Where the rats go SQUEAK,
    And the bats go FLAP!
    And the *skeletons* RATTLE,
    And the ghosts go BOO!

Words: Kaye Umansky
Music: Traditional

4. And continue to FINE

wind — goes — WHOOSH And the — doors — go — BANG! Where the

3. And continue to FINE

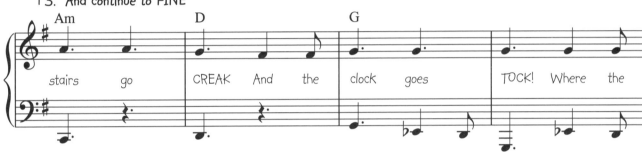

stairs — go — CREAK And the — clock — goes — TOCK! Where the

2. And continue to FINE

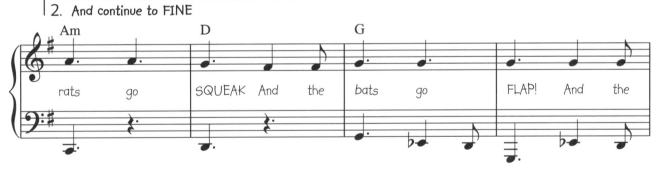

rats — go — SQUEAK And the — bats — go — FLAP! And the

1. FINE

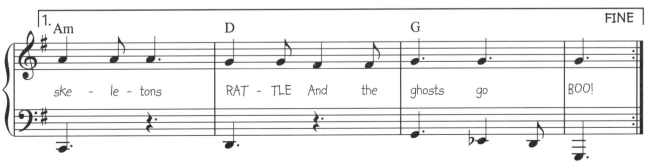

ske - le - tons — RAT - TLE And the — ghosts — go — BOO!

Flap Flap

IT'S GONNA BE HOT

Vs 1 It's gonna be hot, hot, hot, hot,
That's what the weatherlady said.
It's gonna be hot, hot, hot, hot,
That's what the weatherman said.
It's time for the
T shirts, T shirts,
Beach ball, beach ball
Paddling pool, paddling pool,
Sun! Sun! Sun!
It's gonna be hot ...

Vs 2 It's gonna be wet, wet, wet, wet ...
It's time for the
Raincoat, raincoat,
Wellies, wellies,
Wet play, wet play,
Rain! Rain! Rain!
It's gonna be wet ...

Words and music: Jane Sebba

It's gon - na be hot, hot, hot, hot, That's what the wea-ther -la-dy said. It's gon - na be hot, hot,

hot, hot, That's what the wea -ther -man said.
1. It's gon - na be
2.

MAJĀ PADE

Vs 1 Rainfall, rainfall, dripping and splashing,
Rainfall, rainfall, dripping and splashing,
Let's all be happy, splashing in the falling rain.
Let's all be happy, splashing in the falling rain.
  Varasad, varasād, sarsar varaso
  Varasad, varasād, sarsar varaso
  Majā pade amane – bhijavāni
  Majā pade amane – bhijavāni

Vs 2 Sun shine, sun shine, sun shine in splendour …
Let's all be happy wandering in the sunshine …
  Sooraj sooraj chamko chamko …
  Majā pade amane – faravāni …

Words and music: Niru Desai

1. Rain__ fall,__ rain__ fall, drip - ping and splash - ing, Let's all be
Va - ra - sād,__ va - ra - sād, sa - r - sa - r va - ra - so, Ma - jā pa -

hap - py,__ splash - ing in the fall - ing rain.
- de a - me - ne__ bhi - ja - vā__ ni.

GONNA BUILD A HOUSE BOAT

Rain rain go away
Year 2 track 62

Gonna build a house boat,
  gonna *build* it fine,
Gonna *build* it right, so I hammer in time.
Tap tap tap tap goes the hammer,
Tap tap tap tap goes the hammer,
Tap tap tap tap goes the hammer,
Oh Noah, gonna *build* it fine.

Gonna build a house boat,
  gonna *build* it fine,
Gonna *build* it right, so I saw in time.
  Zzz zzz zzz zzz goes the woodsaw ...

Gonna build a house boat,
  gonna *build* it fine,
Gonna *build* it right, so I chisel in time.
  Chip chip chip chip goes the chisel ...

Gonna build a house boat,
  gonna *build* it fine,
Gonna *build* it right, so I paint in time.
Wish wash wish wash goes the paintbrush ...

For more songs like this visit www.acblack.com/musicexpress

NOAH'S ARK

Vs 1 Noah built an ark, he went and built an ark,
He took a saw and hammer and he went
and built an ark.
And it sounded just like this! (Interlude)

Vs 2 They came in two by two, they came in
two by two,
God sent the animals, they came in two by two,
And it sounded just like this! (Interlude)

Vs 3 The rain began to fall, the rain began to fall,
The waters were a-rising as the rain
began to fall.
And it sounded just like this! (Interlude)

Vs 4 The waves were very high, the waves
were very high,
The ark kept a-floating, tho' the waves were
very high.
And it sounded just like this! (Interlude)

Vs 5 They drifted on the sea, they drifted on the sea,
All around was water as they drifted on the sea.
And it sounded just like this! (Interlude)

Vs 6 Noah sent a dove, a raven, then a dove,
She brought him back an olive branch, Noah sent
a dove.
And she sounded just like this! (Interlude)

Vs 7 Noah's safe at last, Noah's safe at last,
He's safely back on land again,
Noah's safe at last.
And it sounded just like this! HOORAY!

Words: Kaye Umansky

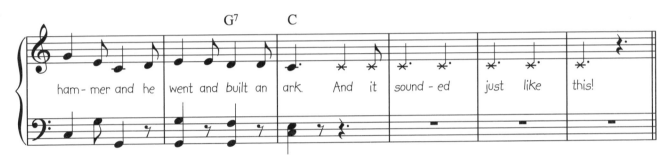

59

POST CALYPSO

Here comes the postie,
Out very early,
Up with the bright sun,
Off on the post run,
Rat tat tat tat tat,
Card on the doormat,
Sounds like they're having fun.

Words: Sheena Roberts

For more songs like this visit www.acblack.com/musicexpress

JUST A LOAD OF RUBBISH

Feel around in my big box,
Take your time ... (pause)
What have you got?
Just a load of rubbish but it makes a
   lovely sound
Shake it high, shake it low, shake it all
   around.

Words and music: Veronica Clark

SALLY GO ROUND THE SUN

Sally go round the sun,
Sally go round the moon,
Sally go round the chimney pots
On a Monday afternoon, Hoi!

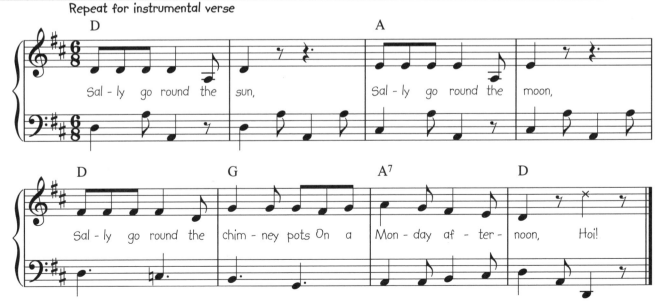

Photocopying is illegal **61**

TEATIME SHOUT

Ch Let's make a meal for a hungry little
sister,
Let's make a meal for a hungry little
girl.
What shall we make for a hungry little
sister?
What shall we make for a hungry little
girl?

Vs 1 Oh, tap on the saucepan lid and shout,
curry for me, curry for you,
Oh, tap on the saucepan lid and shout,
curry for me and you.

Ch Let's make a meal for a hungry little
sister ...

Vs 2 Oh, scrape a potato skin and shout,
chips for me, chips for you ...

Ch Let's make a meal for a hungry little
sister ...

Vs 3 Oh, shake up a pan of maize and shout,
popcorn for me, popcorn for you ...

Words (adapted from traditional): Sheena Roberts

WHEN I GO TO BED

Vs 1 When I go to bed I lie as quiet as a
mouse,
And listen to the friendly noises drifting
round the house.

Vs 2 The far-off sound of talking and the
creaking of the floor,
Music from the radio, the banging of a
door.

Vs 3 The sound of people's footsteps as
they walk along the street,
Clicks and creaks and rumbles as the
radiators heat.

Vs 4 Cups and saucers clinking as they're
washed and put to dry.
Barking dogs and yowling cats, the
buzzing of a fly.

Vs 5 The rumbling sound of traffic and a
sudden noisy laugh,
Splashing from the bathroom as my
sister has a bath.

Words and music: Veronica Clark

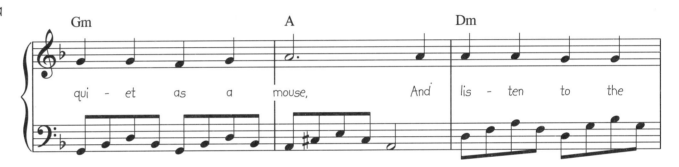

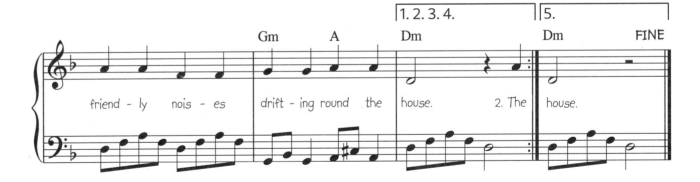

ACKNOWLEDGEMENTS

The publishers would like to thank everyone who assisted in the preparation of this book: Katherine Davies, Michael Haslam, Jocelyn Lucas, Carla Moss, Sheena Roberts, Jane Sebba and Michelle Simpson.

The following copyright material has been created for **Music Express** by A&C Black or is previously published in A&C Black publications:

Bang, bang the sticks go bang, Choose an instrument, Clap your hands and wiggle your fingers, Make your sound like mine and **Some sounds are short** words by Sue Nicholls from *Bobby Shaftoe, clap your hands*, published by A&C Black © 1992 A&C Black.

Down the avenue, Fade or float, **Jenny tap the sticks** (*Jenny play the drum*), **Silence and Sound, Sound puzzle** and **When you play the tambour** words by Sue Nicholls from *Michael Finnigin, tap your chinigin*, published by A&C Black © 1998 A&C Black.

Fossils in the rock words by Helen MacGregor from *Listening to Music 5+*, published by A&C Black © 1995 A&C Black.

Hands can hold and hands can squeeze words by Veronica Clark to traditional melody, from *High Low Dolly Pepper* published by A&C Black © 1991 A&C Black.

How many people here for dinner? Post calypso (words), **Teatime shout** (words) by Sheena Roberts created for *Music Express* © 2002 A&C Black.

It's gonna be hot words and music by Jane Sebba from *Songbirds: SEASONS*, published by A&C Black © 1997 A&C Black.

Just a load of rubbish and **When I go to bed** words and music by Veronica Clark, from *High Low Dolly Pepper*, published by A&C Black © 1991.

Pinocchio words by Kaye Umansky from *Three Tapping Teddies* published by A&C Black, © 2000 A&C Black.

Start conducting (words), **Looby Loo** (verses 2 and 3) by Helen MacGregor created for *Music Express* © 2002 A&C Black.

Shall I sing? (April showers) words adapted from traditional by Helen MacGregor and Sheena Roberts, music by Neville Favell, from *Harlequin* published by A&C Black.

The Hairy Scary Castle and **Noah's ark** by Kaye Umansky, **Yo ho ho, me mates** and **Jack's song** by Helen MacGregor from *Three Singing Pigs*, published by A&C Black © 1994.

Dipidu from *Tinderbox*; **I hear thunder** and **Hot cross buns** from *Sing Hey Diddle Diddle*; **I am the music man, I jump out of bed in the morning, Miss Mary Mac, Okki-tokki-unga, Six little ducks, Someone's in the kitchen with Dinah** and **This old man** from *Okki-tokki-unga*; **Jackass wid him long tail** and **Tinga layo** from *Mango Spice*; **Kye kye kule** from *Songbirds: ME*; **Pease pudding hot** from *Flying a Round*; **Rillaby rill** from *Birds and Beasts*; **Rain rain go away** and **Sally go round the sun**: traditional words and melody, arranged by A&C Black.

The following copyright holders have kindly given their permission for the inclusion of their copyright material in this book:

Coming down by Jill Darby © 1980 BTW Music.

Five little froggies adapted from traditional by Helen MacGregor, from *Five little frogs* arranged, produced and recorded by Playsongs Publications © 1998 Playsongs Publications.

Ho! Jack Frost words by Helen Call, Music by Mary Root Kern © 1941 (renewed) Summy-Birchard Music, a division of Summy Birchard Inc, USA. Warner/Chappell Music Ltd London W6 8BS. Reproduced by permission of International Music Publications Ltd. All Rights Reserved.

I can see coconuts adapted with new words by Helen MacGregor from *I can see cherries* by Wendy van Blankenstein.

It's bonfire night by Leslie Lees from *Jump in the Ring*. By permission of Ward Lock Educational Company Limited.

Listen to the east words and melody by Sheena Roberts © 1995 Sheena Roberts.

Lots of worms words and music by Patty Zeitlin © Bullfrog Ballades, used by permission of Folklore Productions Inc.

Majã pade words and music by Niru Desai © 1982 Niru Desai.

Prehistoric Animal Brigade © words and music by M L Reeve. Used by permission of the M L Reeve Estate.

Says the bee words and music by Malvina Reynolds. Copyright 1961 by Schroder Music Co Renewed 1989. Used by permission. All rights reserved.

Sing a song of people words copyright Lois Lenski 1956, music by Chris Cameron, published in *Tinderbox* by A&C Black © 1982.

The slide song words and music by Sue Nicholls © 1992.

Slowly, slowly words traditional, melody (*Slowly walks my grandad*) by A W I Chitty, Paxton Music Ltd, arranged and recorded for Sleepy Time Playsongs by Playsongs Publications. All rights reserved.

Sound song words and music by Harriet Powell from *Game-songs with Prof Dogg's Troupe* created by Ed Berman, published by A&C Black Publishers Ltd. Used by permission.

The wheels on the bus arranged and recorded for Sleepy Time Playsongs by Playsongs Publications © 1995 Playsongs.

Every effort has been made to trace and acknowledge copyright owners. If any right has been omitted, the publishers offer their apologies and will rectify this in subsequent editions following notification. (The publishers regret that it has not been possible to trace the copyright owner of **Gonna build a house boat** or of **Mi caballo blanco**, attributed to Francisco Flores del Campo.)